BLAST

Dee Phillips

Evans

First published in 2009
by Evans Brothers Limited
2A Portman Mansions
Chiltern Street
London W1U 6NR
UK

Printed in Dubai

British Library Cataloguing in Publication Data
Phillips, Dee.
    Blast. -- (Right now)
    1. Graphic novels. 2. Young adult fiction.
    I. Title II. Series
    741.5-dc22
    ISBN-13: 9780237539535

Developed & Created by Ruby Tuesday Books Ltd

Project Director – Ruth Owen
Head of Design – Elaine Wilkinson
Designer – Alix Wood
Editor – Frances Ridley
Consultants – Lorraine Petersen, Chief Executive of NASEN, and Antony Loveless

© Ruby Tuesday Books Limited 2009

ACKNOWLEDGEMENTS

With thanks to Lorraine Petersen, Chief Executive of NASEN for her help in the development and creation of these books.

Images courtesy of Shutterstock; **pages 10-11, 13, 16-17** Antony Loveless; **pages front cover, 8-9, 25, 34-35, 42-43** Superstock.

While every effort has been made to secure permission to use copyright material, the publishers apologise for any errors or omissions in the above list and would be grateful for notification of any corrections to be included in subsequent editions.

We were under attack.
The enemy was firing at us.
One of our guys was hurt.
I had to rescue him...

BLAST

ONE MOMENT CAN CHANGE YOUR LIFE FOREVER

The sun is hot on my face.
I'm standing up straight,
but my legs are shaking.
I'M SO SCARED!

I've never felt so scared.

I'm looking straight ahead.

I try to stop my legs shaking.

The sun hurts my eyes.

I can't believe this is happening.

I CAN'T BELIEVE I'M HERE...

I'm Private Ed Collins.
I'm a soldier.
It's all I ever wanted to be.
I wanted to protect my friends.
I wanted to fight my enemies.

It happened three months ago.
It was getting dark.
Our platoon was moving
slowly back to camp.

I was inside the turret of our vehicle.
I was manning the gun.
I was on the look out for trouble.

It was cold and dark.
The only noise was the rumble
of our platoon.

13

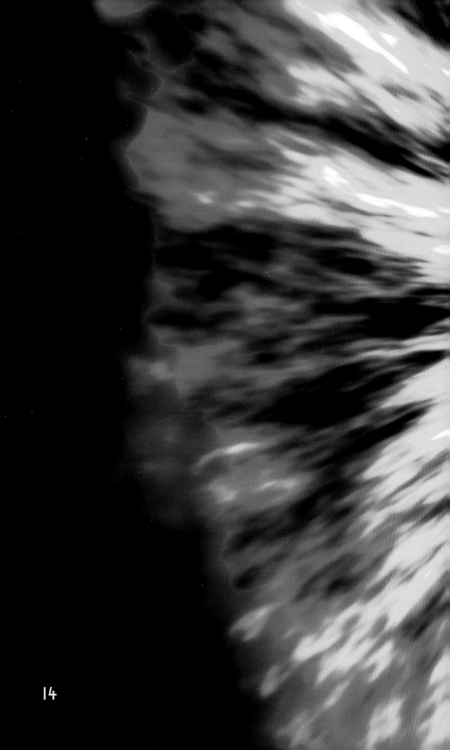

BOOM!

Suddenly, there was a huge blast.

The vehicle in front
had been hit by a huge
home-made bomb.
We were under attack.

There was fire and
smoke everywhere.
The vehicle in front
was a ball of fire.
Was anyone inside
it still alive?

Enemy fighters were firing at us.
They were hidden behind some trees.
I fired back.
I kept on firing.

Bullets hit our vehicles.
Our soldiers fired into the trees.
Suddenly, I saw something...

Over by the trees.
It was a soldier.
One of our guys.
He was crawling away
from the burning vehicle.

But he was crawling straight
towards the enemy!

I had to rescue him!
I grabbed my rifle.
I jumped down onto the ground.
I ran low and fired into the trees.
Bullets flew past me.

I screamed, **"COVER ME!"**

I made it to the soldier.
It was Private Dan Johnson.
He was on fire!

He screamed, "Help me!"
I rolled him in the sand to put
out the fire.
He was badly burned and his
legs were hurt.

Another soldier ran up to us.
It was Private Liz Carter, the medic.

BANG!

A grenade exploded close by.

Carter screamed, "We have to move him. NOW!"

Bullets were hitting
the ground all around us.

I said, "OK, mate. Hold on."
I lifted Johnson.
I lifted him onto my
shoulders.

I screamed,

"COVER US!"

We ran for
the vehicles.

Machine gun fire

Explosions

Our soldiers
fired back.

WE MADE IT!

Carter got to work
helping Johnson.
I got back inside the
turret and looked around.

The enemy was closing in.
We had to get out.
We had to get out now!

The attack seemed to go on forever.
Then our planes came.
They fired on the enemy.

Our helicopters rescued us.
We got out.
All of us got out.

The sun is hot on my face.
I'm standing up straight,
but my legs are shaking.

I'M SO SCARED!

I've never felt so scared.

I'm looking straight ahead.

I can see Private Johnson smiling at me.
He's in a wheelchair but he is going to be OK.
Soon he will be able to walk again.

I stand up straight.
Here she comes.
This is it.

She says, "Well done.
Your fast thinking and bravery
saved Private Johnson's life."

She pins a medal to my chest.

I salute.
I'm Private Ed Collins.
I'm a soldier.
It's all I ever want to be.

43

LIGHT AND DARK
ON YOUR OWN

Look at how dark shapes and colours are used on pages 10–11 and 36–37.

- Make your own art using dark shapes. Use paints, pastels or inks to create a colourful background on plain paper.

- Draw shapes on to black paper. Keep the shapes simple and strong.
- Cut out the shapes, arrange and stick them onto your background.

TRUST IN ME
WITH A PARTNER

Trust is very important in an army platoon. Play this game to find out how far you can trust your partner!

- Create a minefield by scattering bean bags in a cleared area.
- Put on a blindfold. Your partner must guide you through the minefield by giving directions with his or her voice only.

FACING FEARS
IN A GROUP

On pages 4 and 38 Ed says, "I've never felt so scared." In your group discuss:

• Why do you think Ed is more scared about getting the medal than he was during the fighting?

• How do you think Ed feels when he gets his medal?

• Have you ever done something you were scared to do?

• How did you feel before, during and after you did it?

DREAM COME TRUE
ON YOUR OWN / WITH A PARTNER / IN A GROUP

Ed dreamed of becoming a soldier so that he could protect his friends and fight his enemies.
Make your dream come true!

• Think of something that you really want to do.

• List some reasons why you really want to do it.

• What will you need to succeed?

• What might stop you succeeding – can you overcome this?

IF YOU ENJOYED
THIS BOOK,
TRY THESE OTHER
RiGHT NOW!
BOOKS.

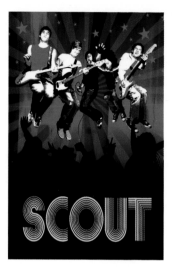

Tonight is the band's big chance. Tonight, a record company scout is at their gig!

Tonight, Vicky must make a choice. Stay in London with her boyfriend Chris. Or start a new life in Australia.

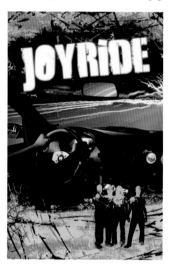

Dan sees the red car. The keys are inside. Dan says to Andy, Sam and Jess, "Want to go for a drive?"

It's Saturday night.
Two angry guys. Two knives.
There's going to be a fight.

Sophie hates this new town.
She misses her friends.
There's nowhere to skate!

It's just an old, empty house.
Lauren must spend the
night inside. Just Lauren
and the ghost...

Today is Carl's trial with
City. There's just one place
up for grabs. But today,
everything is going wrong!